'The goldfish are looking a bit peaky,
Since you cleaned them with spot-remover.
And I don't want to spend another two hours
Getting the gerbil out of the hoover.'

A hilarious and inventive collection of poems and stories – from a mum who doesn't want any more help (how *do* you go about getting a gerbil out of a hoover?), to a genie in the television, to the ballad of Dan Turnip, and much, much more. Funny, rude, thoughtful and often outrageous, this is Jerome Fletcher's first book to be published by Corgi Books.

# A GERBIL IN THE HOOVER

The poems 'I Eat My Dog With Relish', 'The Elbow That Came to Dinner' and 'My Bottom Talks to Strangers' were first published in Jerome Fletcher's book *Alfreda Abbot's Lost Voice* (1988) and are reprinted by permission of Oxford University Press.

A GERBIL IN THE HOOVER

A CORGI BOOK 0 552 52588X

First published in Great Britain by Doubleday, a division of Transworld Publishers Ltd.

PRINTING HISTORY
Doubleday edition published 1989
Corgi edition published 1991

This book is set in Garamond by Chippendale Type Ltd., Otley, West Yorkshire.

Corgi Books are published by Transworld Publishers Ltd., 61–63 Uxbridge Road, Ealing, London W5 5SA, in Australia by Transworld Publishers (Australia) Pty. Ltd., 15–23 Helles Avenue, Moorebank, NSW 2170, and in New Zealand by Transworld Publishers (N.Z.) Ltd., Cnr. Moselle and Waipareira Avenues, Henderson, Auckland.

Made and printed in Great Britain by The Guernsey Press Co. Ltd., Guernsey, Channel Islands.

# A GERBIL IN THE HOOVER

Poems and stories by

## Jerome Fletcher

Wittily illustrated by Nick Sharratt

**CORGI BOOKS**

# CONTENTS

*This book is lovingly dedicated
to Magda Groszek and her
digestive system*

I wonder if you might help me. A lot of people have said what a wonderful poem I am, and I was hoping I might appear in this book – on this page perhaps, or somewhere nearby?

*Sorry, mate, there's not enough room here. Try page 26. I think that's empty.*

Oh, splendid!
Thank you.

# THE SONG OF THE LONELY NOSE

A rather sad, overweight nose stands alone
In the playground, getting frozen,
Watching them playing their games all around,
And wondering why *it*'s never chosen.

It desperately wants to join in, you see,
But nobody takes it seriously,
Because it's no good at games.

It finds it hard to hit a ball,
And can't catch a frisbee that's spun.
Football's too fast for a nose that's so vast,
But it loves nothing more than to run.

'That's not what's at issue,' they say to the nose.
'We know that noses can run.
The problem is just that you're so fat and slow,
You always spoil our fun.'

Nobody cares, nobody knows,
Nobody'd mind if it stood there and froze.

It doesn't whinge if it gets dirty,
And it's not afraid of getting kicked.
It's just a nose that wants to be chosen,
Just a lonely nose that wants to be picked.

# THE SOAP OPERA – EPISODE 46

'What's the story so far, then?'

'Well, it all began with A
Who's extremely rich,
Who's married to B
(She's a bit of a bitch).
B hates A, and has
Fallen in love with D.

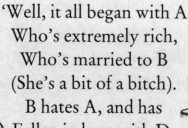

A finds out and,
In a fit of jealousy,
He buys a gun and
Tries to murder D.
But when that fails,
A runs away to sea.

Now, D is going out
With C at this time,
And C is busy planning
Her own little crime,
Because C has a sister,
Who just happens to be B, see?

What C is after
Is all B's moneeeey,
Plus the chance of revenge
On the dirty D.
For this, she gets some help
From a bloke named G.

Then this man called E turns up.
And here the fun begins,
'Cause D and E turn out to be
Identical twins.
So I'm never really certain
If it's D or E I see.

Meanwhile, there's F
(That's A's first wife),
We all thought she'd drowned,
But a dolphin saved her life.
When she returns from the dead . . . '

'All right! Enough! I'm afraid I haven't followed
A single word you've said!
But all these people seem to me
A rather nasty group.
And the storyline is like
A bowl of Alphabetti soup!

I'm thoroughly confused.
It's enough to make me gasp!
Are they called *soap* operas
'Cause they're so difficult to grasp?'

# THE DREAM

'What's happened to you then, Byram?' asked his friend, Maurice.

Maurice had been sitting on the bank of the canal, fishing. He had just put a fresh fish finger on his hook and cast it back into the water when Byram Blunderbuss had hopped into sight with a big bandage round his foot. Byram sat down on the bank next to Maurice.

'What's happened to your foot?'

'I dreamt last night that I stood on a piece of broken glass,' said Byram. 'It hurt so much in my dream that this morning I decided to put a bandage round it.'

Maurice burst out laughing at Byram.

'What's so funny? You wouldn't be laughing if it'd happened to you,' said Byram, mournfully.

Maurice stopped laughing and gave his friend a smug look.

'Sometimes you can be really stupid, you can,' he said.

'Oh yeah! And what d'you mean by that, then? I didn't know there was going to be a piece of glass in my dream, did I?'

Maurice answered with a sneer.

'Yeah, but only somebody really stupid like you would go to bed without his shoes on! It's all your own fault, Byram!'

Byram sat looking sullen and moody for some time.

'Anyway,' he said finally, 'when I trod on the glass in my dream, you walked past me and I called out and you wouldn't even come and help me. Some friend you are!'

Maurice seemed upset by this accusation. He squirmed a little, then said: 'Sorry, Byram. It was just that I was too busy in *my* dream to hear you.'

'Huh!' Byram sniffed. 'And what was so special about *your* dream that you couldn't help a friend?'

Maurice took on a very superior air and replied, 'Actually, I was going to have tea with the Pope.'

'Oh sure!'

'It's true. He asked me if I liked baked beans and I said yes. Then he said did I want them cold or hot, and I said I wanted them hot.'

Byram's mouth was beginning to water with all this talk of baked beans.

'I bet they were delicious!' he said.

'I don't know,' Maurice replied, somewhat sheepishly. 'The trouble was it took such a long time for them to get heated up that I woke up before they were ready.'

Byram laughed triumphantly at his friend's misfortune.

'Now I wish I'd asked for them cold,' Maurice said, looking miserable.

'Why didn't you stay asleep longer?' asked Byram, who found it difficult to understand how anybody could have passed up the chance of a plate of baked beans.

Maurice was getting fed up with being reminded

about the food he had missed. But this talk of dreams did bring to mind an extraordinary tale he had heard recently.

'Did I tell you about this bloke I heard about, who dreamt he was about to have his head chopped off?' he asked Byram. 'And somebody came in to wake him up and touched him on the neck. And the bloke who was dreaming thought he really had had his head chopped off and he died of fright!'

Byram looked at Maurice, his mouth gaping open, astonished by this extraordinary story. He did not know how to reply. He looked down at the grey waters of the canal. Then he said, 'Here, Maurice!'

'Yeah.'

'I think you've caught a fish finger.'

# MY BOTTOM TALKS TO STRANGERS

My bottom talks to strangers,
It talks behind my back.
It sometimes only whispers,
But I can hear it black-
ening my name.

People usually pass it by,
Ignore it, aren't amused.
But some will say: 'The cheek of it!'
And think they've been abused.
Or worse.

For those who stop and listen,
It tells tales about my past.
It knows I get embarrassed,
But that just makes the tales last
Even longer.

I just can't shut it up. You see
The predicament I'm in.
Once my bottom starts to blabber,
All I can do is grin,
And bear it.

# A MAGGOT

I often wondered what it's like to be a maggot.
I asked myself, 'Is this the life for me?'
I'd never even spoken to or met one.
So in the end I thought I'd go and see.

Well, I can tell you . . .

Maggots' manners quite disgust me,
And I'd rather not discuss the
Reasons why they must kee-
p wriggling around in slime.

They're useless at gymnastics,
Hopeless at mathemastics,
Their spelling's not fantastics,
And they don't know how to rhyme.

Maggots' bodies make me snigger,
As their tummies grow much bigger.
Trying to improve their figure
Is just a waist of time.

All in all, they're a very boring bunch.
Still, it must be fun to live inside your lunch.

*Unfortunately, since this poem first appeared a large number of letters have been received from many different places complaining about its contents. Some people feel that the poem is unfair to maggots. They feel that it paints a distorted and unpleasant picture of what maggots are really like. We would like to make it clear that we have no desire to offend anyone or anything that wriggles. So, out of fairness, we have agreed to include in this section some of the letters of complaint that have been received. These are printed on the next two pages.*

Noo York City,
Noo York,
U.S.A.

Dear Sir,

I read your pome about the maggit with innerest
and, dammit! I didn't like what you had to say
about these good friends of mine. I have lived
in the Big Apple here for the best part of
twenty years and never have I come across a
borin' maggit. In my opinion, they is friendly,
innerestin' and talented. Once a month I go
fishing with a whole crowd of them, and usually
tney catch more fish than what I do. So I don't
wanna see no more pomes about dumb maggits!

Yours,

*Hubert R. Bollweevil III*

Hubert R. Bollweevil III

Plumstone
Essex

Dear Sir or Madam

I am writing to complain in the strongest possible terms about your poem 'The Maggot'. It may surprise you to know that we are not just lazy, useless creatures who sit around all day eating our own homes. There have been maggots in Plumstone since the fifteenth century. One of my ancestors, Sir Pelham Maggot, was the designer of the London Underground. Another, more distant, relative invented the Gruyère Cheese while he was on holiday in Switzerland. And who was the first manufacturer of bath sponges? One Arnold Maggot, that's who! It is about time that people started appreciating the contribution that we have made in all walks of life, rather than dismissing us as slimy, disgusting or laughable.

Yours Sincerely

Maggie Squirm (Mrs.)

# THE AMOEBA'S SONG

*(This poem has been magnified 10,000 times.)*

Oh, life is good and life is fine,
Living in this pond of mine.
Any food I swallow whole,
Engulf it in my vacuole.
When I move (it's never far)
I spread my pseudopodia.
I'm not in love, and that's quite smart,
Because I haven't got a heart.
Oooh! Something odd is happeninging
I'm beginninging to cocome apartpart
I I'm turningurning into to two two.
I'm no I'm longer no longer on my on own my own.

| | |
|---|---|
| Hello, who are you? | Hello, who are you? |
| I am me and I am you | I am me and I am you |
| And you are you and you are me. | And you are you and you are me. |
| Oh, life is good and life is fine. | Oh, life is good and life is fine. |
| Living in this pond of mine. | Living in this pond of mine. |
| When I move (it's never far) | Any food I swallow whole, |
| I spread my pseudopodia. | Engulf it in my vacuole. |
| I'm not in love, and that's . . . | I'm not in love, and that's . . . |

*STOP! STOP! STOP! STOP! Do you realize what would happen if this poem continued like this? Well, I suggest you think about it! It has taken about thirty seconds to read the poem, and during that time it has doubled. At the beginning there was only one of them. Now there are two. This means that at the end of ten minutes there would be . . . let me just work it out . . . yes, there would be 1,342,177,256 poems. They would fill something like 180,000 books, and we'd have to cut down four Canadian forests to make enough paper. I think you'd better move on to the next poem quickly.*

25

# QUEEN BOADICEA

Pardon me, but I was told a while back that there might be a spare page for me around here. I am a poem of the highest quality, and between you and me, I'm a lot better than most of the feeble verses that have appeared so far in this book.

*I don't know who told you there was any space here, but I'm afraid you've been misinformed. There's a poem called 'Queen Boadicea' appearing here. Try further on. Page 48 is free.*

Bold Queen Boadicea of Britain
Enjoyed a bit of a laugh,
Riding around in her chariot,
Chopping the Romans in half.

As she left the house in the morning,
Her husband would ask in the hall,
'Where are you off to, O Queenie?'
'Just going out shopping, that's all.'

She'd get in her two horse-power chariot
And roar round the bypass hell-bent,
Annoying the other road-users
And cutting them up as she went.

The Romans didn't find this amusing.
'Got no sense of humour, these folk.'
But Bobo soon had them in stitches,
'Oh, there's nothing quite like a good joke.'

Outside the new supermarket,
Most sensible people would park.
But Bo went in straight through the doorway
And rode up and down for a lark.

'Everything's far too expensive.
Just look at the cost of this rice!'
So she spurred on her two mighty horses
And charged around slashing the price.

'That's better!' said Queen Boadicea.
'It's quite a bit cheaper in here.
I'll have twenty-four slices of bacon,
A large chop and half a pig's ear.'

Queen B. exploded with anger,
When asked to pay for her buys.
'They're getting too stroppy, these Romans!
They ought to be cut down to size.'

Back home, the Queen said to her husband:
'Unload the chariot, you berk!
I'm off to lie down for an hour.
Chopping is such tiring work!'

# JOURNEY TO THE LAND OF LOST WORDS

'What is this place?' we asked the man,
As we stood upon the hill,
Looking out over field and wood
As the morning lay quite still.

'What is yon strange creature called,
And what are those strange birds?'
The man he turned and answered us:
'That is the Land of Lost Words!'

We'd travelled many a gruelling day,
To find this fabled land,
As as we walked on now we knew
Our goal was close at hand.

The Customs-men they welcomed us,
But warned: 'You must not stay
Beyond old Ashen Faggot Night
Or Skirisfurisday.'

Down the happy highway we
Set off in merry twosomes,
And met a sackless nirrup there,
Suffering from yewcums.

'What brought this on?' we asked of him.
He looked at us and sighed.
'A kibble of kewny chammocks, sir,'
He boked as he replied.

We took the nirrup as our guide
And listened as he told
Us of the curious creatures here
And wonders to behold.

We vamped about the countryside.
The nirrup led the way.
He stopped to chat to a hodmadod
Up to its knees in hay.

A Bamsey sat outside her house,
Watching her ahmoo chew.
A gladdigoaster trundled up
And bowed to let us through.

The airymouse flew overhead
As night began to gather.
All around, the lazy nurks
Lay deep in slub and blather.

Then suddenly the nirrup baulked
And fled, consumed with fear.
He'd spied a surly, black-eyed man,
Who snarled as he drew near.

On his back was a wriggling sack.
We asked, 'What's in your bag?'
The man replied: 'A goodly catch!
Two prindles and a scag!

I hunt down words and capture them,
And when I've got enough,
I sell them to the BBC.
They appear on "Call My Bluff"!'

# IT'S NOT MY FAULT!

The Headmistress was sitting at her desk signing reports and, as usual, the door to her office was slightly open. Hearing the sound of footsteps in the corridor, she looked up and happened to notice Mr Rowntree as he walked past her open door with what looked like a lead in his hand. Mr Rowntree was followed a very few moments later by a large penguin.

Followed by a what?

You heard me. A penguin. In fact, a penguin with a lead round its neck. This lead led the Headmistress to wonder if perhaps there was some connection between Mr Rowntree and the penguin. She jumped to her feet, rushed to the door and shouted after Mr Rowntree: 'What on earth are you doing with that . . . creature?'

He turned round and answered her: 'I'm putting him in detention, Headmistress.'

'You're putting him in detention!' she repeated, not quite believing what she had been told.

'Yes, I'm putting him in detention.'

'Why, Mr Rowntree, are you putting a penguin in detention?'

'Because it's his fault,' he replied.

The penguin looked first at Mr Rowntree, then at the Headmistress, then at Mr Rowntree again.

'What is his fault?' asked the Headmistress, folding her arms.

'Well,' began Mr Rowntree, eager to tell his tale. 'I was giving a lesson today and had my back to the class when someone let out a piercing scream. I turned round and everybody was looking at Belinda Harding. "Belinda, I will not have people screaming in my class," I said. "You will go into detention for an hour this afternoon." "There's a mouse in my bag," she shrieked. "And Byram Blunderbuss put it there." So I told Byram in that case he would go into detention instead. But he replied that it wasn't his fault. Maurice had made him do it. Maurice then said that it wasn't his fault, because he'd bought the mouse from a pet shop and if the owner hadn't sold it to him he couldn't have given it to Byram. So I went to visit the pet shop and the owner said that it certainly wasn't his fault. He didn't usually buy mice. However, that week the mouse supplier was selling his mice at a very cheap rate. If they hadn't been so cheap he would never have bought them. So I went to see the mouse supplier and he said that it wasn't his fault because his mice

normally go to the zoo as food for the animals. But this week the zoo hadn't ordered as many mice as usual, so he was left with a lot that he had to sell off cheaply. So I went to the zoo and the head keeper said it wasn't his fault that he hadn't ordered as many mice as usual. The fact was that this penguin had refused to eat his fish so there was a whole lot of fish left over that the keeper fed to the other animals instead of mice. So I went up to the penguin and explained to him that if he hadn't refused to eat his fish, none of this would have happened. But the penguin said nothing. It stood there and refused to say a word. Well, you know me, Headmistress. Not one to put up with that sort of insolence! So in the end I had no choice. I came to the conclusion that this was all the penguin's fault and that's why I'm putting him in detention.'

Mr Rowntree stood looking at the Headmistress. He had a broad grin on his face and was obviously pleased with himself. The Headmistress put her hands on her hips and looked severe.

'Have you gone completely mad, Mr Rowntree?' she asked.

He was not a little surprised by this question. 'I don't think so, Headmistress!' he replied.

The Headmistress sighed. 'What day is it today, Mr Rowntree?'

'Tuesday, Headmistress.'

'Tuesday, Mr Rowntree. How many times do I have to keep reminding you that there is no detention on Tuesdays? You will take that penguin away and bring him back tomorrow, when there *is* a detention.'

Mr Rowntree slapped his forehead and looked embarrassed.

'Yes, Headmistress. Sorry, Headmistress.'

The Headmistress shook her head as she watched Mr Rowntree and the penguin waddle off down the corridor to the main doors of the school. It's extraordinary, she thought to herself. That man has taught in this school for ten years and he still can't remember that there are no detentions on Tuesdays!

## AN EXPRESSION OF CONFIDENCE
## FROM A FATHER DODO
## AS HE WATCHES
## HIS BROOD OF LITTLE DODOS
## SCRABBLING AND
## WHIFFLING
## AMONG THE SUGAR CANE
## IN THE YEAR OF OUR LORD
## 1678

As I watch over Elmer, Marie, Ted and Trevor,
I know that we Dodos will go on for ever.

36

# DIALOGUE OF THE DEAF

## Monday

*I don't know why he bothers.*
*He never listens to what I say.*
*Without taking his nose out of his paper, he'll ask:*
*'So what did you do today?'*

'So, Sam, what did you do today, son?'

*There! What did I tell you!*

'Well, Dad, let me see . . .
I killed a fire-breathing dragon,
And rescued a damsel in distress,
Who turned out to be the postman,
Wearing a pink chiffon dress.

I fought most of the night with a monster,
About the size of Loch Ness.
The garden was swimming in blood by dawn . . . '


'I hope you cleared up the mess,
And didn't leave any bits on the lawn.
I don't work all weekend in that garden
Just for you to untidy it again.'


'No, Dad.'


**Tuesday**


'So what did you do today, Sam?'


'Well, Dad, let me see . . .
Oh yes! Me and my friend, Andy,
Started World War Three!
We began by invading Portugal.
(That was just before tea.)
Then later on, in an armoured car,
We devastated the USSR . . . '

'I hope you tell your mother where you are,
And don't go off on your own?
And I think he's a bad influence on you,
that boy Andy!'

'Yes, Dad.'

## Wednesday

'Well, son, what did you get up to, today?'

'Ummmmm, now what did I do?
I locked Granny and Granpa in the coalhouse,
And cousin Alice in the loo.
I buried Uncle Walter,
Though he wasn't entirely dead.
Tomorrow I'm running away from home . . . '

'I think it's time for bed.
You've had a long day today, Sam,
And you need your sleep.'

*Why do I bother, eh?*

# THE BALLAD OF DAN TURNIP

Dan Turnip he read far too much,
When he was still a lad.
The books he read did him no good,
In fact, they did him bad.

For they were tales of highwaymen,
Of desperate thieves and bold,
And young Dan swore he'd join their band
Before he got too old.

Dan's parents they were sore aggrieved
When told about his plan.
His mother wept, his father prayed
And said these words to Dan.

'A highwayman! You must be mad!
A job like that was fine
A hundred years ago maybe!
Not 1989!'

But Dan arose and he replied:
'It matters not to me.
I've got the hat, the mask and gun.
A highwayman I'll be!'

He bought himself a sturdy steed,
Black Betty she was called.
In truth, she was a moped.
'Twas all he could afford.

So off Dan rode, at modest speed,
To start his life of crime.
He found himself a roadside caff
And hid to bide his time.

With pistols primed, Dan waited till
A coach hoved into view.
He leapt aboard, tripped on his cloak,
And his hat went all askew.

As Daniel scrambled to his feet,
He saw that things were grim.
Forty-five ugly football fans
Grunted and snarled at him.

As Dan tore off along the road,
Chased by a howling mob,
He wondered if it might be best
To find another job.

What happened when he tried again
To Dan was all a haze.
A group of OAPs put him
In hospital for days.

By now, young Dan was desperate to
Commit some wicked deeds.
He sneaked into a shop one night
And stole a pound of cheese.

'I must escape immediately.
To Bolton I must fly.
To cover up this awful crime
I need an alibi.'

Dan sprang into Black Betty's seat,
His mind in such a state,
He lost his way at once, and so
Reached Bolton three weeks late.

Dan Turnip went back home at last,
Hung up his mask and gun.
'A highwayman I'll never make.
I'm now a wiser son.

'In truth, I need a steady job,
A sensible career.
I'll see if there's a training scheme
For a murderous buccaneer!'

# BEBEEP BEEP BEEP BEBEEP

*The following is a translation into Beep language of that well-known and popular poem,* The Hoppopoto-mouse and the Wibblybitt. *For those of you who are not very familiar with Beep language, there are some notes at the bottom of the page which will help you to understand the more difficult parts of the poem.*

Beebeep beep beep beep,
Beebeep, beep beep,
Beebeep beep beep beep beep,
Beep beep beebeep beep!    4

Bippity beeeeeeeeeeeep,
Bippity beep beep beep,
Bippity beeeeeeeeeeeep,
Bippity beep beep beep.    8

Beep Bippity beep beep,
Beep, beep, beeeeeeeep.    10

Notes

Line 2        Unfortunately, there is not an exact word in Beep language for a Wibblybitt. This was the closest word available, and really refers to 'a long-haired, tree-climbing animal which uses its long, trunk-like nose to swing from branch to branch.'

Line 3     The second word in this line has been deliberately misspelt. It is not a printing error.

Line 4     In the opinion of many people, this line must refer to the Hoppopotomouse. However, I should point out that it's not the Hoppopotomouse that has smelly feet, but the Wibblybitt. On the other hand, it seems unlikely that a Wibblybitt would eat nothing but cabbage leaves. In the original poem, of course, it is just as confusing. So I shall leave it to readers to make up their own minds about this question.

Line 6     I suspect that this line is intended as a joke and should not be taken too seriously.

Line 7     This is very similar to the sound made by a motor car.

Lines 9 & 10     These two lines translate particularly well into Beep language and are generally regarded as the loveliest in the whole poem. This final image of the Hoppopotomouse and the Wibblybitt singing love songs to each other in the middle of the boating pond as the sun goes down behind the jam factory is simply beautiful. A more tender scene is not to be found anywhere in all Beep poetry.

Line 11     There isn't a line 11, stupid! However, you may have noticed two gaps, between lines 4 and 5 and between lines 8 and 9. If you wish to, you can fill these in with shovelfuls of rubble and bits of broken brick.

# MAY WHATEVER YOU DO NEXT
# CONTINUE UNTIL DAWN

Aha! An empty page at last! So, dear reader, let me begin by introducing myself. I am entitled . . .

*Oi! What do you think you're up to? Just shut up and get out of here! Can't you see there's a story about to start?*

'Rats!' said Belinda as she pulled the knife out of the back of her piggy bank and a twopence piece fell into the small pile of coins that lay on her bed. She counted the coins.

'Not enough to buy a plug, let alone a whole stereo system!' she whined. Belinda shook the pig angrily. The rattle told her that there were only a few more coins left inside. She sat on the edge of her bed and pouted. 'If only my fairy godmother were here!' she said.

No sooner had the words left Belinda's lips than a small glow began to appear in the middle of her tiny bedroom. This glow got bigger and bigger and brighter and brighter until there, dressed in a brilliant white gown and carrying a wand in her hand, stood Belinda's fairy godmother.

'Why are you looking so sad, Belinda?' asked her fairy godmother, tenderly.

'Oh, fairy godmother,' she replied. 'I have spent so much money on flowers for the sick children, and I bought my granny and granpa such an expensive gift for their wedding anniversary, and I gave such a lot of my money to the Donkey Hospital, that now I don't have enough left to buy my little brother a birthday present.'

As she spoke a large tear appeared at the edge of her eye and rolled down her cheek.

'There, there!' said her fairy godmother, putting an arm round Belinda to comfort her. 'As a reward for all your goodness I am going to give you a little blessing. May whatever you do next continue until dawn.'

And with that, the fairy godmother waved her wand, letting fall a shower of golden sparkle, and disappeared.

Now, if you believed what Belinda was saying – all that nonsense about flowers for sick children and presents for Granny and Granpa and donations to the Donkey Hospital – you'll believe anything. It's just a huge pack of lies. And what is extraordinary is how someone as unpleasant as Belinda managed to get a fairy godmother in the first place! I always thought they only appeared to good little children who were poor and had wicked stepmothers! Obviously not. Anyway, Belinda wasn't feeling any better now than she had been before her fairy godmother appeared.

'A fat lot of good she was!' said Belinda. 'What's the use of a fairy godmother if she won't even lend me a fiver! Ah well, never mind. Let's see how much is left in this pig.'

Belinda picked up her piggy bank and, with the knife, she began to prise out the remaining coins through the slit in his back. Each time a few came out, Belinda was convinced that that was the last of them. But no. Something very strange was happening. She kept shaking the piggy bank to discover that there were still a few more coins inside. And Belinda continued to prise coins out of the piggy bank all night long, just as her fairy godmother had said. It was only as the sun peeped over the horizon and filled Belinda's bedroom with the rosy glow of dawn that the piggy bank no longer rattled when she shook it. It was now empty, but on the bed was a huge pile of coins. Belinda clapped her hands with glee.

'Now I can go and buy that stereo system I've always wanted! Oh, thank you, fairy godmother! And if that scummy little brother of mine thinks he's going to listen to it, he's got another think coming.'

Belinda scooped the pile of coins into a large plastic bag and set off for the shop. But on the way there, she was stopped by the huge and terryifying Byram Blunderbuss. He asked her threateningly, 'What have you got in the bag?'

Belinda opened her bag to show Byram the stash of coins. His eyes lit up.

'Blimey, Belinda! Where d'you get all that dosh from?'

'I've got a fairy godmother. She gave it to me.'

'Oh, sure! 'Course you have! Well, I think you

stole it and you better give it to me, or else I'll . . . '

Belinda swung her bag of cash at Byram and bashed him round the head with it, sending him crashing to the pavement.

'Now, that's what I call spending power!' said Belinda, looking down at the hapless Byram. 'Perhaps it'll teach you to keep your grubby little hands off my dosh!'

And Belinda continued on her way to the shop.

On her way back from the shop, she came across Byram again. He was sitting on the pavement, rubbing his head and nursing a black eye. He looked so miserable that Belinda's heart softened.

'Sorry I had to bash you with my cash, Byram. Still, it was your own fault. I tell you what, next time my fairy godmother appears I'll send her round to you, and perhaps she'll do for you what she did for me.'

Belinda explained the words her fairy godmother had uttered, and how once she had started counting her coins she couldn't stop until dawn, by which time she had a painted shipload of money.

A few weeks later, Byram Blunderbuss got the shock of his life when the small bright glow appeared in his bedroom and grew before his eyes into Belinda's fairy godmother.

'Don't be afraid, young Byram. I am here to help you. Belinda has told me all about your black eye, how you were collecting money for orphans when those wicked boys attacked you and took it all. Some people have no shame. Well, as a reward I shall make a little wish for you. May whatever you do next continue until dawn.'

And with that, the fairy godmother disappeared. Byram Blunderbuss got quite beside himself with excitement at the thought of all the things he'd be able to buy after tonight.

'However,' he said to himself, 'if I'm going to be up all night counting my savings, I'd better just go to the toilet first.'

During the night Byram's mum got up and went to the bathroom. She knocked on the door and called out: 'Byram, are you all right? You seem to have been in there an awful long time.'

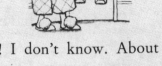

'I'm not feeling too well, Mum. How long is it till dawn?'

'What a strange question! I don't know. About three hours, I suppose.'

From inside the bathroom, Byram Blunderbuss let out a pitiful groan. 'Three hours! Oh no!'

Hang about! What's going on here?
Who was it turned on the light?
What do you think you're up to,
Giving me such a fright?

Yes, you! I'm talking to you, mate.
You with this book in your paw!
And what are you gawping at anyway?
Ain't you ever seen a poem before?

You realize you woke me up, you did.
I was lying here all nice and snug.
Then all of a sudden the page opens up,
And I'm looking at your ugly mug.

I only stopped off for a quick kip,
On my way to some other book.
Now I can't remember its title,
And I don't have a clue where to look.

What's more, I'm not sure that I like you.
You look like a bit of a creep!
So, if you don't mind, turn over the page
And allow me to go back to sleep.

We apologize to the reader for the offensive behaviour of that last poem. As the poem itself has admitted, it is not meant to be in this collection at all. It somehow slipped in between two pages unnoticed and we are doing our best to find out where it came from and which book it should be in. Unfortunately, the poem refuses to move until we have found out where it should be. However, if any reader has an old exercise book with empty pages in it, this poem would be very interested to hear from you. In the meantime, we would like to assure our readers that we would never deliberately allow such a rude, ill-mannered poem to appear in any of our books. Thank you.

# FUBARS

Fubars are wicked and you never know what
to expect.
Under a microscope even, their presence is
hard to detect.
But you know they are around, because they
show you no respect,
And they'll do things to you which make you
feel as small as an insect.
Really, once they creep into your life, they're
not easy to eject.

Fill your mouth with cereal and a fubar will
make you cough,
Unleashing a soggy, gobby spray over Granny's
tablecloth.
Buy some new clothes and a fubar will introduce
them to a moth.

Act cool with a group of girls and a fubar will
knock your glasses off.
Revenge? Don't even think about it! A fubar
will simply scoff!

For all I know, there may be a couple of fubars
in this pome . . .
Sorry, I meant – in this peom . . . dammit! . . .
in thos peom . . .
What's the matter with this typewriter? . . . in
thos piem . . . Rats!
I only bought it the other day . . . in them pios
. . . And it's gone
Wrong already . . . in thes piem . . . Oh,
forget it!

# OH, PLEASE, MUM

'Oh, please can I do the washing-up, Mum?'

'It's very nice of you to ask,
But you know you get over-excited
When I tell you to do this task.
You've smashed more than ten plates already,
Plus all the glasses we got from your gran!
And was it entirely necessary
To use a blowtorch on the non-stick pan?'

'All right then, I'll do some housework.'

No, I'd rather you left it to me.
I think you went slightly over the top
Washing *inside* the TV.
The goldfish are looking a bit peaky,
Since you cleaned them with spot-remover.
And I don't want to spend another two hours
Getting the gerbil out of the hoover.'

'I could give you a hand in the garden!'

'Garden? What garden? That mud patch
out the back?
It used to be green and luxuriant,
Now everything's turning black!
I don't know where you got that weed-killer from!
There should be a warning on the box.
It's powerful enough to kill oak trees,
And, I suspect, melt rocks.'

'I'll clean your car then, Mum.'

'DON'T GO NEAR THAT MACHINE!
I still haven't paid the repair bill
From the last time you gave it a clean.
Using a Brillo pad on the paintwork
Wasn't one of your brighter ideas.
And would you kindly tell me why
You removed all the pistons and gears?'

*There was a time Mum made a law*
*That every day I did a chore.*
*She doesn't make me any more.*
*I can't imagine why not!*

# EARLY MORNING NOISES 1

If you listen to your belly
When you drink a cup of tea\*,
It sounds like the mighty Zambeezee†,
Roaring, rushing
and gurgling,
down to
the
sea.

\* *Government Health Warning*: The
Chief Medical Officers Department
would like to point out that it is very
dangerous to listen to your belly and
drink tea at the same time. Under no
circumstances should you try this on
your own without proper medical
supervision.

† The 'mighty Zambeezee (not to be
confused with Zambezi or Zambesi)'

was a legendary African river that used to rise in the jungles of the Belgian Congo (which is now called Zaire). From there, it flowed for 1,500 miles across the plains of Malawi, Tanzania (which used to be called Tanganyika) and Zambia (which used to be called Northern Rhodesia) before disgorging itself into the sea at Port Baira, Mozambique (which used to be called Weston-super-Mare). At its widest the river measured 20 miles, and at the Victoria Falls it dropped a spectacular 350 feet from a plateau into the jungle below.

In 1856, an expedition led by Colonel Edward Clopton Sproke set out to find the source of the mighty Zambeezee. This expedition, organized by the Royal Geographical Society, left from Port Baira with a team of bearers and guides, numbering 300 in all. The early stages of the journey were easy enough. The expedition made swift progress across flat, fertile plains that spread out on either side of the gently flowing river. Later, the going became slower and more dangerous, the river more turbulent. There was the constant fear of attack from hostile tribes or wild animals. Many of Colonel Sproke's expedition fell victim to a mysterious sickness.

After two months, the expedition found itself in thick jungle, which it had to hack a way through. This slowed its progress down considerably. It sometimes took the explorers all day to cover one mile. Just when everything was at its most desperate, Colonel Clopton Sproke came upon the magnificent waterfall. At that time the falls were called M'Baningi Wana, which in the language of that region meant 'The Devil's Carwash'. A few years later, somebody else (Dr Livingstone, I presume) came along and discovered the falls for the second time. He renamed them the 'Victoria Falls' after his favourite railway station.

Finally, on 26th July 1857, after a perilous and arduous eight-month journey, his expedition decimated by mutiny, Arab slave traders and fever, Colonel Clopton Sproke stumbled into a clearing in the jungle and found what he had been searching for – the source of the mighty Zambeezee! Unfortunately, this turned out to be nothing more than a tap that somebody had left dripping. In a fit of rage at having wasted so much time and effort, Colonel Sproke turned the tap off and four months later the once-mighty Zambeezee dried up for ever.

# THE GENIE

Byram Blunderbuss rushed home from school, switched on the television and sat down eagerly in front of it. Wednesday. The best afternoon of the week. Byram's favourite cartoon. As the screen glowed into life, Byram saw this face looking out into the room. It was a dark face, with sharp features. On its head it wore a red Turkish hat with a black tassel. The face suddenly noticed Byram and fixed him with a steely stare. This made Byram feel uncomfortable. He

had never been stared at by a face in the television before. The face spoke:

'Oh Great One! O Illustrious Master! I am yours to obey.'

Byram looked around to see if there was anybody else in the room. No. He was on his own.

'Are you talking to me?' he asked the face.

'Yes, O Brave, Bold and Beautiful Byram! I am the Genie of the Television. Your wish is my command, and in return you will help me to escape from this prison.'

Byram wasn't taken in by this for one moment. He knew that genies only appeared out of bottles, not television sets.

'I don't believe you,' he said. 'If you're a genie, prove it.'

'Very well,' replied the genie. He thought for a moment, then said: 'I shall make you a cucumber sandwich.'

Byram suddenly looked petrified.

'No, no. Don't do that!' he wailed. 'If you make me a cucumber sandwich, someone might come along and eat me!'

The genie raised his eyebrows and tutted.

'I didn't mean I'd *turn you into* a cucumber sand-wich. I meant I shall make one *for* you.'

'Oh, right. That's different.'

And all of a sudden there was a cucumber sandwich, lying in Byram's lap. He looked at it, unimpressed and unconvinced.

'That's not very clever,' Byram said. 'Even I can make a cucumber sandwich. Besides, I hate cucumber.'

'Very well, O Wondrous One! Tell me how I may prove myself. Whatever you wish will be yours!'

Byram stuck his finger in his mouth and thought for a moment. Then he hit upon a really clever plan.

'My wish is,' he said, 'to have two more wishes.'

'You have your wish, O Blundering One!' said the

genie. Byram was amazed. 'Blimey, that was clever! You really *are* a genie! So, how did you get inside the telly?'

'My name is Ibn Ivri Wairmun. My father was the Emir of Sumwir and Sultan of Nowir. My elder brother, Walid, whose heart is as black as the desert night, overthrew our father and took his kingdom, where he now rules with cruelty and terror. He sold me as a slave to the wicked Vizir, Ramon, who taught me some knowledge of the black art. But the beatings I received at his hands were a high price to pay for the knowledge I gained. Truly, I would have died in that place, O Bulbous One. I would even have taken my own life, had it not been for the tender kindness of the Vizir's beautiful daughter, Ramona. She cared for me and protected me from the worst excesses of her father's cruelty.

'Finally we resolved to escape together. Ramona told me of the existence of a series of rooms in her father's palace which it was forbidden to enter on pain of death. There she was sure we would find the means of escape. One room we found full of gold, another was full of bloody corpses of the Vizir's victims. In a third, a small twig lay on a shelf, together with a stone and a flask of water. Ramona told me to carry these objects. Other rooms contained horrors or marvels too numerous to speak of here. In the last of the rooms we found a winged horse, and just as we had mounted it to make good our escape, the Vizir discovered our treachery. The horse soared into the air and the Vizir dispatched a giant to catch us and destroy us. Despite the speed of the horse, the giant was getting closer and closer. So Ramona, from the

back of the horse, threw the twig in his path, and instantly a thick wood grew up, which slowed the giant down. But it was not long enough before he was close upon us again. This time Ramona threw the stone in the giant's path, and instantly a huge mountain range sprang up, which he had to climb over. But it was not long before he had caught us up again. Then Ramona cast the flask of water in his path, creating a huge lake into which the giant stumbled and drowned.

'Even then our troubles were not at an end. A great storm blew up and in the buffeting that shook our horse, Ramona lost her grip and fell headlong to earth. Many days I spent searching for her, without success. Finally I came upon a wretched hovel beside a river. There lived an old woman who took me in and fed me. Little did I realize the fate that she was preparing for me . . .'

'Quite an interesting life you've led, really!' Byram interrupted. He was getting impatient with this story.

'Ah, all this happened over a thousand years ago. There is still much to tell.'

It occurred to Byram that if the genie was going to tell his whole life story, they'd be here till the crack of doom and he'd miss his favourite cartoon programme.

'We've got to get you out of the telly,' he told the genie.

'Ah, O Globular One, that may prove a hard task indeed!'

'Nah,' Byram replied confidently, as he left the room. He returned a few moments later with a large hammer. Only too late did the genie realize what Byram's plan was. As he called out a warning, Byram swung the hammer through a wide arc, straight into

the front of the screen. There was a tremendous shattering and splintering, shards of glass fell with a tinkle and a gaping black hole was left where the screen had been.

Just at that moment, Byram's mum came home from work. She walked into the sitting-room and found Byram standing amidst the wreckage of the television with a hammer in his hand.

'Hello, Mum. I got the genie out of the telly.'

Byram's mum stood in a state of shock, staring at the mess. 'The genie,' she repeated mechanically.

'Yeah. He was over a thousand years old!'

'There was a thousand-year-old genie in our television. Is this what you're trying to tell me, Byram?'

'Yeah.'

Byram's mum, as if still in a trance, left the room shaking her head. Byram sat down to watch his favourite cartoon.

'Oh! Er! I didn't think about that!' he said, looking at the gaping black hole.

# A WET AFTERNOON IN THE MIDDLE OF THE SCHOOL HOLIDAYS

Nowhere to go, nothing to do,
Nobody here but me.
Four hours in front of the telly
And my brain has turned to jelly.
Anywhere else is where I'd rather be.

I've never been so bored since . . . yaaaaaaaaawn!
. . . since the day I was born.

It's not very easy     to     stay     awa . . .
. . . ZZZZZZZZZZZZZZZZZZZZZZZZZZZZZZZZZZZ
Sorry! I dropped off for a mo!
I must go and do something interesting,
Like watching Mum's rubber-plant grow.

Or, on the other hand . . .

I could listen to the sound that a light bulb makes,
Or chat to the speaking clock.
Or I could go outside and get some fresh air,
Then pick a fight with a rock.

I could play hide-and-seek with my shadow,
Or read a book, I suppose.
Or lie in the bath for an hour and a half,
Counting the hairs on my toes.
(Except I haven't got any! Hairs, that is!)

This morning I tried, without much success,
To teach the cat how to talk.
Now there's got to be something better to do
Than seeing how slow I can walk.

I know, I'll go and write a poem . . .
. . . all about being bored.

# CONVERSATION WITH THE DENTIST

'Hello there, Jimmy. Come on in and sit up in the chair. That's it. Now, just lie back and relax. There's nothing to be afraid of. Open wide. I'm just going to put this tube in your mouth to suck up the saliva, then we'll have a look at your teeth. Good! How long is it since you were here last?'

'Urrgllennssthlnnths.'

'That long! You really ought to come and see me more often than that, you know. I shall have to have a word with your mum. What have you been up to since I saw you last?'

'Iyeeenookowkaiinnnehhenorteeeks.'

'Oh, that must have been fun! I used to do that when I was your age. It's a lovely part of the country too. Was the weather good?'

'Ehh.'

'I hope you didn't get lost.'

'Earee. Addertayinnertehawworrrrayz. Nnahdiiawwwehoooih.'

'I hope you didn't poison anybody!'

'Nah.'

'Fine. Well, your teeth are in good shape. Rinse your mouth and spit.'

'Gllglllglllllglllllgllgggllll. Ppptuhhh. Pthuh.'

'Good. That wasn't so bad, was it! Off you go, now. Get your mum to make another appointment for you in a few months.'

'Ehhhye.'

'It's all right, Jimmy, I've finished. You can close your mouth now.'

'Oh yeah! Thanks, Mr Grinder. Bye-bye.'

# COMPETITION!

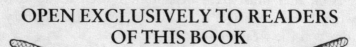

## OPEN EXCLUSIVELY TO READERS OF THIS BOOK

# FABULOUS PRIZES!

### WHAT DO I HAVE TO DO?

All you have to do is to work out exactly what Jimmy is saying while the dentist has got his fingers in his mouth. Write your answers on a postcard and send it in, along with fifteen *Gerbil in the Hoover* book covers. Entries must be in by 29th February 1991.

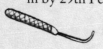

### WHAT DO I WIN?

The first three correct entries out of the bag will win . . . A FREE TRIP TO THE DENTIST OF THEIR CHOICE. There, you will be able to enjoy any filling or drilling that is necessary – ABSOLUTELY FREE!

## HURRY AND SEND IN YOUR ANSWERS TODAY!

# EARLY MORNING NOISES 2

If you eat a bowl of cornflakes
(Without milk, that is),
And amplify the sound,
You will hear the noise of
A Giant's mill,
And human bones
being
g
r
o

u

n

d

# THE FUNNIEST POEM EVER WRITTEN
# SINCE THE DAWN OF TIME

*An Important Message for Our Readers*

*Unfortunately, due to the recent outbreak of Uncontrollable Laughter throughout the country, this poem has had to be withdrawn. The Government is treating* this matter with the utmost urgency in an attempt to keep the situation under control.

Two serious cases of Uncontrollable Laughter have been traced directly to this particular poem. The first outbreak occurred at a school in Nottingham, where twenty-four pupils had to be taken to hospital suffering from Uncontrollable Laughter after reading the poem in class. A week later, three boys and five girls also ended up in hospital after the poem had been handed round a youth club in Colchester.

Young people seem to be especially at risk from this condition because they still have a highly developed sense of humour. Adults generally are in less danger because the sense of humour begins to deteriorate as you get older. Most adults have been able to read this poem without suffering any ill-effects whatsover.

It is important that you are able to recognize a case of Uncontrollable Laughter in its early stages, so that help can be sought as quickly as possible. The symptoms are not very pleasant. The patient suffers from aching jaw, streaming eyes, difficulty in breathing, pains in the chest which often result in the patient being doubled-up and making a rasping noise in the throat. The cure for U.L. is almost as bad as the condition itself. The patient has to spend several days in hospital wearing a pair of headphones, listening constantly to a number of pompous, successful and bossy people (mostly politicians) telling them that life is a very serious business and that they had better pull them-selves together.

Certain government spokespersons have claimed recently that nearly every funny poem in the country is infected with Uncontrollable Laughter. This is simply not true. We must stress that the vast majority of funny poems are quite safe. Ninety per cent of them will not even make the reader smile. It is only in very rare cases, as with the above, that traces of U.L. have been found. For this reason, we have had to withdraw it. We hope this will not spoil your enjoyment of the rest of the book.

Excuse me, but I really must insist that I appear on this page. There aren't many left, and, though I say it myself, I am a great poem: handsome, witty, touching, beautifully put together.

That's as may be, sonny. But you can't stop here. You'll have to move on.

# A SHORT POEM WHICH POSES AN INTERESTING QUESTION, ALBEIT IN A VERY CLUMSY MANNER

Is this a thought that you did ever think?
That to another skunk, a skunk don't stink.

### True Facts About Skunks

The one thing that everybody knows about the skunk, and for which it is rightly famous, is that it can make a horrendous smell. And what is more impressive is that it can spread this smell over a vast area. It can sometimes be smelt up to a mile away, if the wind is in the right direction. For those of you who have never experienced the smell a skunk can make, the following description will give you some idea of

*what it is like. The description comes from the diary of the Reverend Eli Willoughby, who was travelling down the eastern seaboard of the United States in 1786. But first, a word of warning! The smell a skunk makes is so overpowering that it would be safer if you held your nose while you read this passage, just as the Reverend Willoughby had to hold his while he was writing it.*

*14th August.* Cabe across a skunk today! Pffffaaaww! Dat was dizgustig! Dat was de most putrid pong I ever sniffed! Phhheeeeweeeee! What a ronk! It bade by eyes water, I felt dizzy ad I albost fell over. I'd rather walk about wid a old sock up by dostrils! Even if I had a bath for tree weeks in perfube ad rosewater, I still couldn't get rid of dis stench!

Most people assume that skunks have always been able to make this foul smell, but in fact this is not true. There was a time when no well-mannered skunk would dream of making such an offensive stink. However, when it became fashionable for people to wear furs, the skunk saw its beautiful cousins, the silver fox and the mink, trapped and killed in such large numbers that it deliberately chose to go around getting up people's noses. Skunks gained such an unpleasant reputation that no fashionable person dared say to another: 'Don't you just *love* my skunk jacket!' And this is why among the skunks there is a very famous saying, which is taught to young skunks from their earliest years, and which you will find pinned up in every skunk house. It goes:

The surest way to stay alive and well
Is to make a really putrid smell.

# I EAT MY DOG WITH RELISH

I eat my dog with relish,
I like the taste a lot.
A sausage dog is good when cold,
He's even better hot.

I put him into water,
And boil him through and through.
If he's not nice and tender,
He's difficult to chew.

He looks so pink and juicy
As he lies in his bread roll.
I cover him in ketchup
And onions from a bowl.

Now I've finished eating him
I still don't feel full up.
I wish I'd bought a bigger one,
Not just a little pup.

# AT YOUR SERVICE

Byram Blunderbuss had only just started his Saturday job. In fact, this was his first Saturday and he was only doing it because he had to pay his mum and dad for a new television after he smashed the old one trying to release the genie. He was working in a corner shop and he was there simply to serve customers when they came in. To begin with business was slow and Byram spent most of his time whistling, scratching his head or sticking his finger in his ear. Finally, after a while, a customer appeared.

'Have you got any Vick?' asked the customer.

'What?' answered Byram, who still had one finger in his left ear.

'Vick.'

Byram looked puzzled. 'My name's not Vic,' he said. 'It's Byram.'

'No. Do you have any Vick?'

'What's that?'

'It's stuff you rub on your chest when you've got a cold.'

'Nah. We haven't got any.'

'Oh. Well, where can I get some from?'

'I DON'T KNOW. What do you think I am? The *Yellow Pages*?'

The customer immediately turned and walked quickly out of the shop, saying that it was the last time he'd be coming in here. Meanwhile, the owner of the shop had been listening to this conversation.

'No, no, no, Byram. That simply won't do. That's no way to treat a customer. If we don't have what a customer wants, you offer them something similar and say: "I'm sorry I can't help you there, but we do have this. It's best to rub it into your chest when you get into bed. That way you spend all night breathing in the vapours and in the morning you'll feel much better." Something along those lines. Understand?'

'Oh, right,' said Byram.

Byram Blunderbuss spent the next quarter of an hour practising what he had been told. Another customer appeared.

'Have you got any lemon marmalade?' asked the customer.

Byram couldn't find any lemon marmalade, so he picked up a jar of peanut butter.

'I'm sorry I can't help you there,' he said. 'But we do have this. It's best to rub it into your chest just before you go to bed. That way you spend all night breathing in the smell and you'll feel much better in the morning.'

The customer looked at the jar of peanut butter and then at Byram. He asked: 'Why would I want to rub peanut butter all over my chest?'

'TO GET RID OF YOUR COLD, DOTHEAD! Blimey, some people are stupid!'

'But I haven't got a cold!' said the customer.

'WELL, WHY DID YOU ASK ME FOR PEANUT BUTTER, THEN?' Byram shouted.

'I didn't ask you for peanut butter,' said the customer, and he walked out of the shop thoroughly confused.

By this time, the owner of the shop was becoming impatient with Byram. He tried to explain again.

'Look, Byram, in a situation like that you say to a customer: "I'm sorry we don't have what you asked for, sir, but have you tried this instead? You can spread it on toast or dig some out with a spoon and eat it on its own. It's very good with strawberry jam, I believe." That's the sort of thing you say. See what I mean?'

''Course I do,' Byram replied. 'What do you think I am? Stupid?'

Not long after, another customer came into the shop. She looked around for a while, then turned to Byram and asked: 'Er, excuse me. But do you sell red shoe polish?'

Byram could only find a tin of black shoe polish.

'I'm sorry we don't have what you asked for, sir, but have you tried this instead? You can spread it on

toast or dig a spoon in and lick it off the spoon. It's very good with strawberry jam, I believe.'

The woman stormed out of the shop in anger.

'Byram Blunderbuss!' said the owner of the shop.

'Yeah.'

'You're fired!'

# THE ELBOW THAT CAME TO DINNER

An elbow came to dine with me.
Its wits were sharp, its language free.
It told me countless jokes and fibs
And dug into my ribs
of pork.
('Dig in,' I said. 'Help yourself.')
Endlessly that elbow talk-
ed and bored me with its holiday-
s in Elba, Greece and St Tropez.

It drank far too much strong beer
And such a huge amount of wine
It spun around the table,
Singing 'Auld Lang Syne'.

It wouldn't go. It would not leave.
I tried to kick it out.
It leapt into my coffee pot
And got stuck up the spout.

I shoved my hand into the pot
('This elbow is a pain!').
But in the end the only thing I got
Was a nasty dark brown stain
On the tablecloth.

Then Mum's advice came back to me.
(If only I was able!)
'Whenever you are eating, dear,
Keep elbows off the table.'

# SWEARING

*(To be read in a whisper)*

Look, I shouldn't really tell you this,
Because it was told to me
By someone whose name I'd rather not say
Who swore me to secrecy . . .

But if you promise not to tell,
'And I'll kill you if you do,
And I guarantee that she'll kill me
If she finds out that I told you . . .

So you mustn't breathe a word of this.
Cross your heart and hope to die.
You'll probably say I'm making it up,
But I swear it's not a lie . . .

You're not going to believe this, but
Apparently Jane and a friend . . .
. . . What? . . .
. . . Oh, you know already!

# WAVES

Wallo    wa    foll    ea    o
    wing    ves    ow    ch    ther
Billo    cur    sl    bun    toge

Th    fl    t    seag    shriek    a    wat
    ere    oats    he    ull    ing,    nd    ches
wh    b    t    netf    gleam    la    cat

Ris    swe    li    an    hea    or    sai
    ing    ll    fts    d    ves    ange    ls
Slid    hu    dri    an    lea    str    trai

You'll have to excuse me.
I must rush off quick.
Writing this poem
Has made me feel seasick.

# ENDPIECE

Tell me, is this page free? I've searched desperately, for a space in which to appear. But each time I stopped I had my lines chopped, and they threw me out on my ear.

*I'm afraid to say, mate, I think you're too late, 'cause this is the final page.*

Then, please be so kind as to hear a few lines.

*Oh, all right then, but don't take an age.*

I begin in this way: 'As the gold orb of day . . .'

*That is a terrible verse.*

' . . . rises to kiss the child's sleeping bliss.'

*It seems to be getting much worse.*

I can see that I'm faced with a man without taste.

*Yeah, well, here's your coat and your hat.*
*You can take a quick bow,*
*but you'll have to leave now,*
*'cause that, as they say, is that!*

## ABOUT THE AUTHOR

As well as being a writer, Jerome Fletcher has many other talents. He is a Real Tennis professional (and was British Professional Doubles Champion in 1986, 1987 and 1989). He has also been a landscape gardener, an eel catcher and a French and Spanish tutor. This is his second book for children. His first, *Alfreda Abbot's Lost Voice*, was published in 1988. Jerome lives in Southern France.

If you would like to receive a Newsletter about our new Children's books, just fill in the coupon below with your name and address (or copy it onto a separate piece of paper if you don't want to spoil your book) and send it to:

## The Children's Books Editor
## Transworld Publishers Ltd.
## 61-63 Uxbridge Road,
## Ealing
## London W5 5SA

---

Please send me a Children's Newsletter:

Name.................................................................

Address.............................................................

......................................................................

......................................................................